ROYAL
CROWN DERBY
PAPERWEIGHTS
Collectors Handbook

HOWARD BONSER

FJ

FRANCIS JOSEPH
ISBN 1870703-44-8

©Francis Joseph Publications and Howard Bonser 2002
Compiled and written by Howard Bonser

Published in the UK by
Francis Joseph Publications, 5 Southbrook Mews, London SE12 8LG
Tel: 020 8318 9580   email info@francisjoseph.com

Production by
E J Folkard Computer Services, 199 Station Road, Crayford, Kent DA1 3QF

Printed by
Red Design & Print Limited, England

ISBN 1870703 44 8

This book is independently produced by Francis Joseph Publications, London and neither the publishers nor the author have had any input from the Royal Crown Derby factory in the making of this book.

Pricing policy
The prices contained within this book reflect those which apply to the United Kingdom. The current price is the UK recommended retail price and may not apply to all retailers or those overseas. The secondary market price also reflects the prices seen within the UK secondary market. The dollar price shown is to help those in North America assess the likely value of a possible purchase and does not necessarily reflect the price to be expected within the North American secondary market.

Contents

Introduction

Welcome to this, my second book on the Royal Crown Derby Paperweight range. To those who read the first issue I make no apologies for including many of the words from that book here. The issues remain the same and for the newcomer it is better to buy one volume than to have to chase out of date and out of print material. Once again, I have attempted to make a useable and handy reference book that can be easily taken on forays into those smaller recesses of the world of collectable china in the hope of securing that bargain or the missing piece from the collection. The range of Royal Crown Derby Paperweights has continued to expand at an astounding rate, making them one of the most successful ceramic introductions of the twentieth century. For the collector this has been a real problem, as the investment level has had to be high to keep up with the new issues. Any one who has bought each paperweight on introduction will have paid around £15,500 over the twenty-year period.

The main purposes of this book is to help those who, like myself, found it difficult to establish what is and is not a Royal Crown Derby Paperweight. My interest started on our China Wedding Anniversary when I received the original Dragon as a present of from the "Old Dragon"! When I subsequently started collecting them, I did so because I enjoyed owning them and I was most fortunate to start very early on, before the discontinuations started. At this stage I knew nothing about ceramics but as my collection grew, so did my need for information. Searching around I found that most collector books concentrated on the antique market, new china was definitely not in vogue, and relevant information was scarce. The factory was only interested in selling the product and although some retail traders were most helpful, they could not give the full historical perspective. This void is now partially filled by the Collectors Guild, the factory Internet website and the Collectors Guides written by Ian Cox for Royal Crown Derby. But beware, not all that is written is necessarily accurate. Even here, some of the inaccuracies may be perpetuated.

The wider understanding of the production and marking of ceramic objects enables the viewer to correctly identify the maker of an item, it's year of manufacture, painter and guilder. I can recommend the Cox book in this regard, as he was allowed unprecedented access to the factory and its' staff while compiling his data. Such knowledge can add to the enjoyment of ownership, but it is not essential except to avoid the purchase of seconds wrongly identified as firsts. Most of the books about collecting ceramics start from the basis that you have some understanding of the subject before you begin. This I found disconcerting and, therefore, make no apology for starting from the premise that nothing is known. I have produced this booklet to pass on some of the facts I have gleaned, as they relate specifically to the paperweight range, in the hope that those who share my appreciation, know what is available and how to recognise them.

Royal Crown Derby paperweights were introduced at Chatsworth House in 1981 as six animal designs with Imari decoration to compliment other Crown Derby porcelain ware. After a successful launch, they were followed two years later by another six and then four more in 1985. In the years that followed there was an annual increase to the range, which followed the demand, until the present day when there tends to be two yearly introductions in January and June. The withdrawals started in 1987 with three of the range being removed, then a steady annual stream of discontinuations started in 1991 and still occurs. This leaves a range of about fifty different designs available for the purchaser today.

The whole range is eminently collectable and, although they do not qualify as 'antiques' yet, there is evidence that they have established a niche in the secondary market and hold their values reasonably well. There have been some extraordinary prices paid for some pieces, which I cannot believe are fully justified. Over time these prices have been proven not to be sustainable, though there is obviously a premium to be paid if the paperweight is only available on the secondary market. The solution is to wait until you find the piece at a price you are prepared to pay. The cat family has sold extraordinarily well and is therefore quite common, others were less popular and are more difficult to find. John Sinclair, the Bakewell China shop, has established a rare and exclusive commodity into the collection with their first series of special limited editions of 500 copies, which are already highly sought after. These are based on standard paperweights that have been especially painted in different and highly effective colourways. Their second series, the 'Endangered Species' are proving just as popular but are not so rare. There are other specials, by various retailers, which are worth chasing and then there are different backstamps and signatures, which can add to the rarity of the piece. The latest marketing ploy is to have Collectors Events at selected retailers with a special event piece and a member of the factory staff present. This means that it is now quite common for weights to be signed by the modellers and designers at events. In the future, the signatory may become an issue but this is not the case at present.

The definition of a Crown Derby paperweight is becoming more blurred with time. However, as a reasonable guide, each paperweight portrays a creature, is made from porcelain, decorated in an Imari style and is hollow with a hole in the base to enable it to be filled with a suitable material, such as sand, to make it heavier. The hole is usually plugged with a gold plastic stopper embossed with the Royal Crown Derby cypher, though some of the earlier paperweights had china disk cyphers and no stopper. The base is normally marked under the glaze with a year cypher and two further marks identifying the lithographer and gilder. I have included, at the back of this booklet, a list of the relevant cypher marks in use to assist in determining whether or not the paperweight is of an early edition.

This all seems quite simple but there are problems when you try to define exactly what makes up the paperweight range. In a commercial world, there will always be issues limited by number or design. I have already mentioned the special editions commissioned by John Sinclair and there are others by Goviers of Sidmouth, Wheelers of Loughborough, Peter Jones of Derby and Mulberry Hall of York. These are, I believe, a true part of the Royal Crown Derby paperweights. The same applies to issues of paperweights through one particular china retailer, before the full launch date, with the backstamp wording in gold rather than the usual red. Again, it applies to the issues of the Camel, Lion and Zebra, usually limited to between 75 and 150 copies, which have a special Harrods of Knightsbridge inscription. Lastly, I believe that two commemorative pieces should also be included. The first is an issue of 150 copies commissioned by Wheelers of Loughborough in 1994. This, called the **Spirit of Peace** has a white and gold dove descending on a globe being consumed by the flames of war in blues, browns, reds and gold with a scrolled inscription and commemorates 50 years of peace in Europe. The first fifty of these pieces, the gold edition, has the Royal Crown Derby backstamp of the 1940s as well as the current backstamp – the other 100 just the current backstamp. The second is an issue of 2000 copies commissioned by Goviers to mark the start of the third millennium. It is a representation of the fabulous, mythical **Unicorn** in white, seated on a blue base and decorated with gold. The horn is cast in a bronze alloy before being gilded and is the first example of metal being included on a paperweight.

Next to consider are the issue of paperweight blanks painted in the traditional style of the Posie range. This could be interpreted as a different colourway and be accepted as a paperweight, however, it could equally be noted as a different Crown Derby range. Whichever way they are viewed, with the exception of the **King Charles Spaniel**, they were not generally available. Nor did they ever appear in the catalogues. Most were sold in a very close proximity to Derby, so I believe them to be a commercial anomaly. I do not include as part of the range, the six **Tropical Fish** although these are hollow, have stoppers and generally follow the same design rules as the paperweights, with the exception that they all have an identical base in the form of a pale blue seashell. They were also catalogued and sold by Royal Crown Derby as a separate range. But I have included descriptions this time to help those who wish to identify them. The same is not true for the **Dolphin** or the **Golden Carp**, which do form part of the paperweight range. The **Royal Cats** and **National Dogs** are altogether different in both size and conception and, whilst desirable in their own right, they were never intended as paperweights. The same applies to the four heraldic candleholders. Lastly, there are two Crowns. The first a paperweight produced by Royal Crown Derby, in 1990 only, to celebrate the 100th Anniversary of the granting by Queen Victoria of the use of the title 'Royal' to the Derby Crown Porcelain Company in January 1890. The second, the 'Queen Mothers Crown', produced for Goviers of Sidmouth to commemorate Her Majesty's 100th birthday in 2000. Once again, despite their glory, these items are inanimate and should not form part of the range.

In 2000 there was a further trap laid for the unwary, called the **Imaemon Collection**. It was marketed in limited numbers in the UK by Royal Crown Derby. This is a collection of stoneware pieces based on the moulds for the Barn Owl, Cat, Camel, Chaffinch, Goldcrest, Large Elephant, Mandarin Duck, Sitting Duckling, Sleeping Kitten and Rabbit. Each model is decorated in one of three colours, blue, green or grey and then given fresh expression with a polychrome overglaze. The prices for these supposedly limited pieces were very high, from £315 for a sleeping Kitten to £2200 for an Elephant. I say supposedly because the original announcement stated only 110 pieces for the UK and gave limits for each piece. However, on arrival there was an announcement that the actual allocation from Japan differed slightly from the original expectation but gave no detail. I am aware that for the green Mandarin Duck, for instance, which was to have only six available, all six people I knew who had requested one were offered it, and five of those were not known collectors! The UK total has now been declared as 186 pieces out a total of 1500 worldwide. Each piece comes in a Royal Crown Derby box with an inner box made of wood and secured by ribbon but they do not have stoppers, though the hole is there. The factory confirms that these do not form part of the paperweight range but to the collector they could be seen as an expensive curio.

Having realised what is available, a few words on what the prospective purchaser can find may be helpful. Obviously, the largest available stock is first quality examples which are, or have been, sold through retail outlets in Royal Crown Derby boxes. Surprisingly, the box may be the best indication of quality as will become apparent later. Seconds have been sold on to the market and they may generally be identified by a scratch mark through the glaze across the Royal Crown Derby mark. This is, however, not always true, as the scratching through the cypher is a haphazard process done by hand. Other ways of telling a second are that it will have a silver stopper or it may lack a stopper at all. This, however, is not a sure guide as some stoppers may be genuinely lost and I have heard of gold stoppers being re-supplied by the factory, though they assure me that this is not possible. Some of the seconds are very convincing, so when buying on the secondary market always check that you are happy with the decoration and origination of the piece before purchase. A further note of caution for the avid collector is that, though this book shows the dates that paperweights are generally available through all commercial outlets, the factory has produced some paperweights outside those dates to fill commercially viable orders. Those that have, so far, come to my attention are Foxes, Hedgehogs, Owls and Koalas produced between 1993 and 1995.

These minor diversions apart, the paperweight range is eminently collectable and is a wonderful expression of the potters' art. The remainder of the booklet is laid out in alphabetical order, using the given Crown Derby name. This leads to some anomalies such as the Imari Dormouse being under 'I' and the Sleeping Kitten under 'S'. However, if you are really lost, the index at the end is quite comprehensive and tries to group the paperweights into logical 'families'. Each individual entry contains a description of the paperweight with designer information, years on sale, start cost and a guide to the approximate current value or current retail price. These values have been culled from auction results, traders and my own observation to give guidance to the unwary. However, at the end of the day the only reasonable price guide is what you are prepared to pay, realising that the vendor may not be willing to part with the piece for that.

I hope that this information does not weigh too heavily, as the prime aim is to help you identify the product properly so that you can enjoy your collecting more. . .

ARMADILLO

Introduced in 1996 and withdrawn in 1999 this reasonably lifelike representation of the armoured vehicle of the animal world is finished in rich reds, browns and greens of its South American habitat. Not the most usual subject for a paperweight but interesting nevertheless.

Launch Price: £59.95
Secondary Value: £70-£90/$110-$145
Available dates: 1996-1999

ASHBOURNE HEDGEHOG

The second limited edition paperweight by John Sinclair in the Derbyshire series. This colourway on the Hedgehog a somewhat wicked appearance, decorated in reds, browns and greens. It was issued in 1995 and is highly sought after.

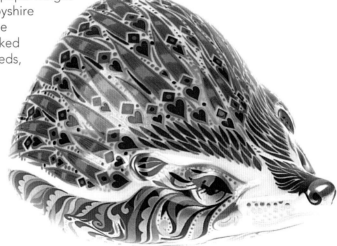

Launch Price: £59
Secondary Value: £750-£800/$1200-$1280
Available dates: 1995

BABY RABBIT

Introduced in 1990 as a Junior paperweight, the baby rabbit is decorated as a miniature version of the rabbit design. Whilst still available it has now become part of the main range, as has the kitten, which was introduced in a similar manner.

Launch Price: £29.95
Current Price: £34/$RRP
Available dates: 1990-Cur

BABY ROWSLEY RABBIT

Produced in 2000 for John Sinclair to pair with the Rowsley Rabbit, it is decorated in the same colourways on the Baby Rabbit mould. As with the larger version this is more endearing than the original.

Launch Price: £42
Secondary Value: £70-£90/$110-$145
Available dates: 2000-2001

BADGER

Produced between 1986 and 1994 the gilded tips on the subtle blue fur of this nocturnal suggest a moonlit lustre. It was re-issued by John Sinclair in 1996 in a different colourway as their third limited edition paperweight.

Launch Price: £53
Secondary Value: £250-£400/$400-$640
Available dates: 1986-1994

BAKEWELL DUCK

This is the first of the John Sinclair specials, which is a colourway variation of the Duck. Issued in 1995, it was sold in the shop over a Bank Holiday and was so popular it almost sold out before collectors knew of its existence. Since then it has been one of the most elusive and expensive paperweights to obtain. It has a very distinctive green head and reddish brown body.

Launch Price: £75
Secondary Value: £1400-£1800/$2240-$2880
Available dates: 1995

BAKEWELL DUCKLING

Issued in 1998 to complement the Bakewell Duck but is not so spectacular or rare. This is a colourway variation on the Swimming Duckling, with the same reddy brown feathers it differs from the original by having green top wing feathers instead of blue.

Launch Price: £48
Secondary Value: £60-£70/$95-$110
Available dates: 1998

BALD EAGLE

A large size paperweight, the Bald Eagle was first taken by Royal Doulton to the USA and was then launched world wide in 1992. Standing proudly on a rock decorated with 1128 Old Imari, the Eagle has feather designs in cobalt blue, red and gold. It is still available today.

Launch Price: £175
Secondary Value: £200-£250/$320-$400
Available dates: 1992-Cur

BARN OWL

A more faithful representation of the natural state than the earlier Owl, this model is shown sitting with the heart shaped face of this silent hunter and delicate feathers in reds, browns, beige and gold. Introduced in 1995 it is still available.

Launch Price: £62.95
Current Price: £78/$RRP
Available dates: 1995-Cur

BEAVER

The national animal of Canada is represented seated with back decoration in cobalt blue and gold whilst the underside has maple leaves and meadow flowers in red on the white background. Introduced in 1994 it is still available.

Launch Price: £49.95
Secondary Value: £80-£110/$130-$175
Available dates: 1994-1997

BENGAL TIGER

Another of the large paperweights, this model shows the king of the forest prowling in his habitat which has been created by using subtle browns and greens with traditional Derby colours. The animal is white with stripes of combined blue, red and gold.

Launch Price: £165
Secondary Value: £250-£320/$400-$510
Available dates: 1994-1999

BENGAL TIGER CUB

This paperweight is similar to the Bengal Tiger in both colour and presentation in red and gold stripes, standing on the forest floor, but is delightfully portrayed pawing a butterfly. Introduced in 1995 it is quite large but is in proportion to the adult. It was pre-launched by Bennets.

Launch Price: £82.65
Secondary Value: £85-£180/$135-$290
Available dates: 1995-1999

BLUEBIRD

This 2000 paperweight was pre-launched by Taylor's of Reigate with a certificate and no special backstamp. Decorated in Imari colours of red, gold and pale blue the bird holds a golden berry in its beak.

Launch Price: £75
Current Price: £78/$RRP
Available dates: 2000-Cur

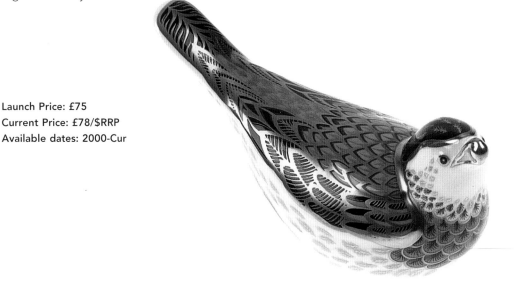

BLUE JAY

Produced as a special request from the home of the Toronto Blue Jays baseball team but available generally. The model is predominantly pale blue with gold feathering on the back with red highlights on the wings, sporting a white breast. It was introduced in 1995.

Launch Price: £59.95
Secondary Value: £70-£90/$110-$145
Available dates: 1995-1999

BLUE LADYBIRD

Another variation on the ladybird theme, this model is predominantly blue with four red and pink spots over blue, brown and beige plants. It was introduced in 1998 and withdrawn in 2000.

Launch Price: £39.95
Secondary Value: £50-£60/$80-$95
Available dates: 1998-2000

BLUE TIT

Introduced in 1994, this cheeky garden bird is shown with its characteristic black and white head, blue and green back feathers and yellow underside all highlighted in gold.

Launch Price: £39.95
Current Price: £52/$RRP
Available dates: 1994-Cur

BROWN PELICAN

Pre-launched by Hadleighs with a special backstamp to mark their 20th anniversary, this bird is depicted standing on the shore with a fish beneath it. With dark brown feathers and gold highlighting the bird looks slightly too menacing to be imposing.

Launch Price: £70
Current Price: £78/$RRP
Available dates: 1998-Cur

BULL

First introduced to the Guild in 1991 and now generally available this is a large size paperweight. Decorated in cobalt blue and gold the bull stands on a china plinth decorated with green grass and an 1128 Old Imari border.

Launch Price: £225
Current Price: £315/$RRP
Available dates: 1992-Cur

BULLDOG

Available to the Collectors Guild in the UK in 1991, the bulldog became generally available in 1992 and is still in production. The seated dog in a traditional, stolid pose is decorated in versions of the Union flag with a large rosette on its back for "Best of Breed".

Launch Price: £75
Secondary Value: £120-£150/$190-$240
Available dates: 1991-1997

BUXTON BADGER

As good as the original, this new colourway was the fourth of the John Sinclair Derbyshire series. It can be told apart from the original model by the blue, green, red and white flashes on its side and the more natural representation of the pelt. Issued in 1996, it is a most attractive model.

Launch Price: £65
Secondary Value: £750-£850/$1200-$1360
Available dates: 1996

CAMEL

This model is a naturalistic representation of the ship of the desert, at rest, kneeling on the sand. Bedecked in tassels and cloths coloured in reds, browns and gold, the bridled and saddled camel looks splendidly benign. In 1996 there was a special version of the Camel produced for Harrods with the firm's logo placed on one of the forelegs.

Launch Price: £245
Current Price: £295/$RRP
Available dates: 1996-Cur

CAROLINA DUCK

Modelled by John Ablitt, the Carolina Duck has a compact shape, strong colouring and distinctive markings. With a green head, red breast and blue back all richly decorated and highlighted with gold this is a splendid addition to the other wildfowl in the range.

Launch Price: £80
Current Price: £82/$RRP
Available dates: 2001-Cur

CAT

The cat, a start of a small dynasty, first appeared in 1985 and remains available. This Japan version with blue, red and gold representing the fur and markings of a cat is seated on its haunches looking benignly upwards, seeking attention. This same model was reissued between 1990 and 1994 in a different colourway as the Ginger Tom.

Launch Price: £53
Current Price: £99/$RRP
Available dates: 1985-Cur

CATNIP KITTEN

Available in 1997 as an inducement to join the Collectors guild, this new colourway for the sleeping kitten is much more likeable than the original. Delightfully decorated in russet and blues it has the plant, catnip, overlaid in gold.

Launch Price: £25
Secondary Value: £50-£70/$80-$110
Available dates: 1997-1997

CHAFFINCH

This cheeky chappie has a predominantly red body with lavish blue and gold highlights on the head and wings which bring to life the common garden sight we all know so well. First introduced in 1989 it is still available.

Launch Price: £41
Current Price: £60/$95
Available dates: 1989-Cur *2002*

CHESHIRE CAT

This third, and weakest, of the John Sinclair first series was a wonderful opportunity missed. Based on, and decorated in the same manner as, the Ginger Tom, it can be identified from the original by a winking eye and a green bow around its neck.

Launch Price: £85
Secondary Value: £600-£650/$960-$1040
Available dates: 1996-1996

CHICKEN

This nesting bird has a white head and neck topped with red comb and wattles. The remainder of its body is decorated in Imari blue, white, red and gold representational plumage.

Launch Price: £49
Secondary Value: £60-£80/$95-$130
Available dates: 1990-1998

CHIPMUNK

First produced in 1986 and still available the chipmunk stands erect on his hind legs. His head and back are decorated with blue and gold reminiscent of fronds of pine whilst the underside has Maple leaves in autumnal shades of red and gold interspersed with golden winged samaras, which are seeds from the same tree.

Launch Price: £33
Secondary Value: £80-£100/$130-$160
Available dates: 1986-1997

COCKEREL

Introduced in 1992 to compliment the chicken and still available, this lord of the farmyard is highly decorated with intricate feather designs in cobalt blue, pale blue, red and gold as befits his station.

Launch Price: £59.95
Secondary Value: £90-£110/$145-$175
Available dates: 1992-1999

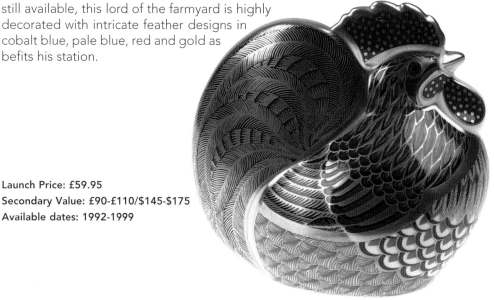

COMPUTER MOUSE

With a decorative pattern reflecting its hi-tech origins decorated in the blues, reds and golds of the traditional Imari, this model is a very successful representation of the most modern of mice. Introduced in 2000 the computer mouse is still available today.

Launch Price: £65
Current Price: £67/$RRP
Available dates: 2000-Cur

CONTENTED CAT

Yet another cat but this is much more appealing and lives up to its title. In red, pale blue and gold scrolled patterns this model, introduced in 1995, gives every feel of the domestic pet.

Launch Price: £59.95
Secondary Value: £80-£110/$130-$175
Available dates: 1996-1998

CONTENTED KITTEN

Introduced in 1996 to follow the successful Contented Cat, this model is completed in the same pattern and colourways of pale blue, red and gold.

Launch Price: £45
Secondary Value: £70-£90/$110-$145
Available dates: 1996-1998

COOT

Introduced in 1995 the coot's feathers are picked out using traditional Derby colours leaving the characteristic white head flash that so often betrays the bird in the wild.

Launch Price: £49.95
Secondary Value: £70-£90/$110-$145
Available dates: 1995-1997

COUNTRY MOUSE

Inspired by the small mouse that can be seen hiding in the decoration of the Lion, this stylised representation of a curled up mouse was modelled and designed by John Ablitt. Decorated with seedpods and other items from the mouse's environment, it is coloured beige, red, blue and gold. A difficult weight to make, so check quality carefully.

Launch Price: £48
Current Price: £48/$RRP
Available dates: 2000

CRAB

A flat but not unattractive representation of this inhabitant of the seashore is decorated with sea anemones, seaweed fronds and limpets to show its rock pool habitat. The crab was available between 1988 and 1991.

Launch Price: £49
Secondary Value: £120-£180/$190-$290
Available dates: 1988-1991

CROMER CRAB

A version of the Crab paperweight produced for, and sold exclusively through, Royal Doulton until the end of 2002, it comes with special backstamp and certificate. Designed by Tien Manh Dinh, it is decorated in turquoise, the blues and browns typifying the seas around the small Norfolk seaside town, renowned for the quality of this edible delicacy after which the paperweight is named.

Launch Price: £95
Current Price: £95/$RRP
Available dates: 2001-2002

DAPPLED QUAIL

This model is a new colourway on the Quail by Louise Adams. This combines a deep rich red with pink, mushroom and black highlighted with gold to accentuate the delicate feathers. An effective piece, it complements the original well.

Launch Price: £78
Current Price: £78/$RRP
Available dates: 1999-Cur

DEBONAIR BEAR

A variation on the Teddy Bear produced as a Collectors Guild exclusive in 1998. This bear has no bow tie, a blue and red lapelled waistcoat with an orange kerchief draped from the pocket. Its footpads match the waistcoat.

Launch Price: £62
Secondary Value: £50-£70/$80-$110
Available dates: 1998

DEER

This is the first model to be exclusive to the new Royal Crown Derby Collectors Club and is a large paperweight. This delicate, seated and alert representation has tan and gold fur with blue markings. The base has various browns and a green worked in with the traditional Derby colours to give the effect of the forest glade. It was only available in 1994.

Launch Price: £150
Secondary Value: £550-£700/$880-$1120
Available dates: 1994

DERBY COUNTY RAM

A representation of the black headed, black legged Derbyshire ram with brown and gold curved horns. The body has a white, blue and black fleece and the model has a similar shape to the large Ram. Sold through Derby County FC in 1998, this variation differs from the Derby Ram by having gold leaves under the fleece instead of the brown. It was sold with a signed certificate.

Launch Price: £54
Secondary Value:
£80-£100/$130-$160
Available dates: 1998

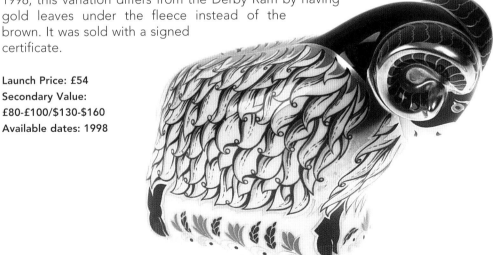

DERBY RAM

A representation of the black headed, black legged Derbyshire ram with brown and gold curved horns. The body has a white, blue and black fleece and the model has a similar shape to the large Ram. Sold through Crown Derby Visitor Centre between 1998 and 2000, this model has green and brown leaves under the fleece.

Launch Price: £58.50
Secondary Value: £70-£90/$110-$145
Available dates: 1998-2000

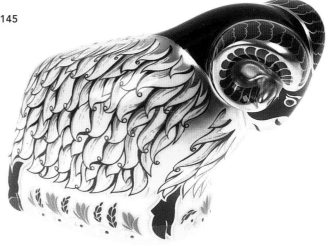

DERBY WREN

This variation on the Wren was produced in 1998 as the complimentary gift for membership of the Collectors Guild. It is recognisable by the red, blue and gold Imari feathers which give it a reddish and more natural hue as opposed to the predominantly blue of the original.

Launch Price: £25
Secondary Value: £40-£60/$65-$95
Available dates: 1998

DERBYSHIRE DUCKLING

This model was produced for John Sinclair in 1999. It is a variation on the Sitting Duckling with predominantly green feathers and is more effective than the original red.

Launch Price: £48
Secondary Value: £40-£60/$65-$95
Available dates: 1999

DOLPHIN

One of the more unusual of the paperweights and the second fish, the dolphin is in a resplendent royal blue with golden curling waves and droplets of sea spray on its back to repeat the curving movement of the dolphin as it glides through the seas.

Launch Price: £57
Secondary Value: £220-£260/$350-$415
Available dates: 1987-1993

DONKEY

Introduced as a signature edition of 1500 called "Thistle" by Goviers in 2000, this model will enter the general range in 2001. Depicted by John Ablitt seated, it has been decked in the style of a Mediterranean donkey with blanket, saddlebags and tassels. Basically white the accoutrements are coloured in brown, beige, blue and gold.

Launch Price: £99
Current Price: £99/$RRP
Available dates: 2001-Cur

DORMOUSE

A very round, handleable and dormant representation of this rare creature. The model is predominantly white and is decorated with forget-me-nots, wild oats, golden corn and barley. Introduced in 1991 it is still available.

Launch Price: £29.95
Secondary Value:
£40-£60/$65-$95
Available dates: 1991-1999

DRAGON

Introduced to coincide with the Chinese year of the Dragon in 1988, this model is richly decorated in a blue, red and gold scale design. It was withdrawn in 1992.

Launch Price: £69
Secondary Value: £210-£260/$335-$415
Available dates: 1988-1992

DRAGON OF GOOD FORTUNE

The second of a matching pair of Dragons forming a limited edition made for Peter Jones in celebration of the new Millennium and the Chinese year of the Dragon in 2000. It is striking and most effective design which is lavishly decorated in turquoise, red and gold with green markings to the head. It is coiled clockwise with the head resting on the spine.

Launch Price: £175
Secondary Value: £160-£190/$255-$305
Available dates: 1999

DRAGON OF HAPPINESS

The first of a matching pair of Dragons forming a limited edition made for Peter Jones in celebration of new Millennium and the Chinese year of the Dragon in 2000. It is striking and most effective design which is lavishly decorated in reds and gold with turquoise and blue markings to the head and body.
It is coiled counter-clockwise with the head raised clear.

Launch Price: £175
Secondary Value: £160-£190/$255-$305
Available dates: 1999

DRUMMER BEAR

This seated Teddy Bear has a drum between his legs and is dressed in a blue military tunic with grey trousers. Introduced in 1998, this version has an Imari pattern around the drum and is still available today.

Launch Price: £80
Current Price: £95/$RRP
Available dates: 1998

DRUMMER BEAR (GOVIERS)

This seated Teddy Bear has a drum between his legs and is dressed in a blue military tunic with grey trousers and is identical to the Drummer Bear except for the decoration of the drum. Available only in 1998, this version has a predominantly red sidewall to the drum with gold inverted "y-shaped" drumhead tensioners.

Launch Price: £80
Secondary Value: £100-£150/$160-$240
Available dates: 1998

DUCK

Introduced in 1981 and still available today, this bird has a base colour of white with intricate feather patterns interpreted in traditional Imari colours of blue and gold to emphasise its subtle form. The model formed the basis of the first limited edition production by John Sinclair in a different colourway in 1995.

Launch Price: £41
Secondary Value: £70-£100/$110-$160
Available dates: 1981-1997

DUCK BILLED PLATYPUS

Produced in advance of the Australian Olympics in 2000 with a Kangaroo and Koala as part of an "Australian Collection", the model depicts this unusual mammal swimming and is coloured in yellows, browns and reds. Those made before the end of 2000 have a gold signature backstamp and a certificate.

Launch Price: £65
Current Price: £65/$105
Available dates: 1999

FAWN

The standing fawn is modeled by John Ablitt and compliments the Deer in tan, blue and gold in a rich Imari style. Available exclusively to members of the Collectors Guild in 1996.

Launch Price: £79.95
Secondary Value: £210-£245/$335-$390
Available dates: 1996

FIRECREST

This model is the Guild complimentary piece for 2000. It is a new colourway on the Goldcrest base with plumage of blue, green red and yellow which mirrors the naturally brightly coloured feathers of the Firecrest. The head flash is yellow as opposed to the red for the Goldcrest.

Launch Price: £27.50
Secondary Value: £50-£70/$80-$110
Available dates: 2000

FOX

Portraying a smug and seated fox, the original issue in a blue decoration represented the fur of the Arctic Fox. It was issued in 1983 and withdrawn in 1987 only to be reissued in a different colourway between 1990 and 1993.

Launch Price: £49
Secondary Value: £350-£450/$560-$720
Available dates: 1983-1987

FROG

Introduced in 1983 and still available today the frog is a lifelike representation of the amphibian in a rich Japan interpretation of an exotic Paisley design seated on a blue and gold pebble.

Launch Price: £53
Secondary Value: £110-£130/$175-$210
Available dates: 1983-1997

GARDEN SNAIL

Issued as a piece for purchase at Royal Crown Derby events in 2000, the Garden Snail is a new colourway design by Tien on the Snail. Resplendent in cobalt blue, iron reds and green highlighted with broad bands of gold this is a much more splendid snail than the original.

Launch Price: £90
Secondary Value:
£90-£120/$145-$190
Available dates: 2000

GINGER KITTEN

This revision of the colourway for the Kitten produces a kitten to complement the Ginger Tom with the same colourings. It is the first of a matching pair produced as a limited edition of 1500 for the Guild of Specialist China and Glass Retailers in 2000.

Launch Price: £56
Secondary Value: £70-£100/$110-$160
Available dates: 2000

GINGER TOM

Another colour way for the cat model, this time in red and gold only with green eyes. Introduced in 1990 as the Ginger Tom, it was withdrawn in 1994 but has become one of the more sought after models.

Launch Price: £45
Secondary Value: £550-£650/$880-$1040
Available dates: 1990-1994

GOLDCREST

Another of the common birds, this bright and cheerful model has blue, red and gold Imari flashing on the head, wings and tail. The body is white with the feathers represented in gold. Introduced in 1991 it is still available.

Launch Price: £29.95
Current Price: £38/$RRP
Available dates: 1991-Cur

GOLDEN CARP

The first representation of a fish, the carp was available between 1986 and 1991. It was followed by a series of Tropical Fish which though made in the same manner were never wholly part of the paperweight collection. Painted in a rich gold and red interpretation of fish scales, the gilding on the mazarine blue base represents a pebbly streambed.

Launch Price: £63
Secondary Value: £200-£260/$320-$415
Available dates: 1986-1991

GOLDEN PHEASANT

One of a pair of very large and unusual paperweights produced to celebrate 250 years of china manufacture in Derby. First issued in 2000 with a signature gold backstamp, it will join the general range in 2001. On a curved base and displaying the best features of this magnificent and highly coloured oriental bird, it is principally a golden yellow with a red breast.

Launch Price: £595
Current Price: £595/$RRP
Available dates: 2000-Cur

GREY KITTEN

Issued as an inducement to join the Collectors Club in 1995, this model is a different colourway to the Kitten and just has the blue and gold stripes without the red.

Launch Price: £25
Secondary Value: £30-£50/$50-$80
Available dates: 1995

GREY SQUIRREL

Yet another special based on the squirrel but, despite its name, it is predominantly blue in colour. Decorated with Hazel bushes with green and white leaves, the red nuts are obviously just ripe enough to tempt the squirrel out for a snack. This paperweight was only available from Debenhams in 1998.

Launch Price: £67.50
Secondary Value: £60-£80/$95-$130
Available dates: 1998

HAMSTER

Decorated in a rich Imari pattern the Hamster had a short run and was available between 1989 and 1992. Principally white, it is decorated with small red fir trees that make it look incongruous. Somewhat overweight and with its pouches filled to capacity, this was not a popular model.

Launch Price: £33
Secondary Value: £80-£100/$130-$160
Available dates: 1989-1992

40

HARBOUR SEAL

Modelled by Robert Jefferson and re-designed by Tien Manh Dinh, the Harbour Seal was the event piece for 2001 in a limited edition of 4500. Decorated in blues and golds on a white base the design reflects the sea spray, bubbles and waves of the Harbour Seal's coastal water habitat.

Launch Price: £85
Current Price: £85/$RRP
Available dates: 2001-Cur

HARVEST MOUSE

This endearing representation of a mouse was available between 1985 and 1994. It is predominantly white and is decorated with fruit motifs of blackberry and Rowan berry with ears of golden corn reminiscent of the autumn fields and hedgerows when one is most likely to catch sight of the creature in the fields.

Launch Price: £29.95
Secondary Value: £40-£60/$65-$95
Available dates: 1985-1994

HEDGEHOG

Another paperweight produced between 1983 and 1987 the hedgehog was an endearing representation of the hedgehog and was decorated with an Imari version of the animal's prickly coat. It was later reused in a different colourway by John Sinclair as their second limited edition in 1995.

Launch Price: £42.50
Secondary Value: £420-£480/$670-$770
Available dates: 1983-1987

HERALDIC LION

Produced exclusively for Goviers of Sidmouth, the Heraldic Lion was designed by Mark Delf and modelled by Louise Adams, to complement the earlier Unicorn. A limited edition of 2000 it shows the animal seated but alert with straight front legs. It is a different model to the Lion paperweight though the colourings are similar.

Launch Price: £180
Current Price: £180/$RRP
Available dates: 2001-Cur

HONEY BEAR

Not as evocative as the Panda, the Honey Bear sits with one leg outstretched. Decorated with a blue and gold body with red and gold fur markings on the legs and cheeks he has a somewhat supercilious smirk. Introduced in 1994 he is still available.

Launch Price: £79.95
Secondary Value: £90-£120/$145-$190
Available dates: 1994-1997

HORSE

Launched in 1990 to celebrate the Chinese year of the Horse, this model this is in Chinese rather than natural style. It is shown seated and is predominantly white with blue and gold decoration and red saddlery. It was withdrawn in 1993.

Launch Price: £57
Secondary Value: £120-£170/$190-$270
Available dates: 1990-1993

HUMMINGBIRD

The hummingbird is posed as though on a branch. Its back is decorated with cobalt blue, pale blue, turquoise and red feather patterns leaving the breast to red feathers, the whole being highlighted in gold. Introduced in 1993 it is still available.

Launch Price: £49.95
Secondary Value: £70-£90/$110-$145
Available dates: 1993-2000

IMARI DORMOUSE

The same model as the dormouse is given the Imari treatment in cobalt blue and gold. It was introduced at the same time but looks neither as comfortable nor as interesting. It was withdrawn in 1993.

Launch Price: £39
Secondary Value: £80-£110/$130-$175
Available dates: 1991-1993

IMPERIAL PANDA

The first in the second series of John Sinclair's special editions called "Endangered Species", this paperweight is a new colourway on the original panda. They may easily told apart as this model comes with a certificate and it has bamboo decorated onto its chest with red and blue flowers defined in gold on the arms. It was produced in a limited edition of 1000 in 1998.

Launch Price: £89
Secondary Value: £100-£120/$160-$190
Available dates: 1998

KANGAROO AND BABY

Produced in advance of the 2000 Australian Olympics with a Duck Billed Platypus and Koala as part of an "Australian Collection", this model depicts the mother Roo with the "joey" peeking out of the pouch. It is coloured in the same browny reds of the Deer and is a naturalistic representation. Those made before the end of 2000 have a gold signature backstamp and a certificate.

Launch Price: £125
Current Price: £130/$RRP
Available dates: 1999-Cur

KING CHARLES SPANIEL

This sad eyed and somewhat doleful spaniel is generally white decorated in blue and gold representations of the dog's coat. A 1993 introduction it was withdrawn in 1996.

Launch Price: £63
Secondary Value: £60-£90/$95-$145
Available dates: 1993-1995

KINGFISHER

Sitting on a pebble decorated with small flowers the kingfisher holds a small golden fish in its beak. The bird itself has rich feather decoration in cobalt blue, turquoise, red and gold. Introduced in 1993 it is still available.

Launch Price: £63
Current Price: £84/$RRP
Available dates: 1993-Cur

KITTEN

The kitten was introduced as a Junior paperweight in 1990 and is designed and decorated in a similar manner to the cat. Whilst still available it has now become part of the main range, as has the baby rabbit, which was introduced in a similar manner.

Launch Price: £49
Current Price: £60/$RRP
Available dates: 1990-Cur

KOALA

Introduced to honour the Australian Bicentenary in 1988 and withdrawn in 1993, this loveable bear has a blue decoration gilded with sprays of the eucalyptus, its favourite food, and a somewhat puzzled expression.

Launch Price: £57
Secondary Value: £200-£240/$320-$385
Available dates: 1988-1993

KOALA AND BABY

Produced in advance of the 2000 Australian Olympics with a Kangaroo and Duck Billed Platypus as part of an "Australian Collection", the model depicts this unusual bear with its baby on its back coloured principally white with gold fur climbing a eucalyptus tree. Those made before the end of 2000 have a gold signature backstamp and a certificate.

Launch Price: £90
Current Price: £95/$RRP
Available dates: 1999-Cur

LADY AMHERST PHEASANT

One of a pair of very large and unusual paperweights produced to celebrate 250 years of china manufacture in Derby. First issued in 2000 with a signature gold backstamp, it will join the general range in 2001. On a curved base and displaying the best features of this magnificent and highly coloured oriental bird, it is principally black and white with a blue back and golden breast.

Launch Price: £595
Current Price: £595/$RRP
Available dates: 2000-Cur

LADYBIRD – 2 SPOT

Small, round and very much the ladybird found eating the aphids in the garden, this model has a red back with one large and one small black spot on each wing cover. It was introduced in 1997 as one of a pair and was withdrawn in 1999.

Launch Price: £34.95
Secondary Value: £60-£80/$95-$130
Available dates: 1997-1999

LADYBIRD – 7 SPOT

Small, round and very much the ladybird found eating the aphids in the garden, this model has a red back with three black and white spots with a red centre on each wing cover, with the seventh spot on the centre line just above the head. It was introduced in 1997 as one of a pair and is still available today.

Launch Price: £34.95
Current Price: £42/$RRP
Available dates: 1997-Cur

LAMB

Introduced in 1992 and still available today, the lamb is predominantly white with a cobalt blue face to match the Ram, the fleece is decorated in pale blue and gold to compliment the Ram and the Sheep.

Launch Price: £45
Secondary Value: £60-£80/$95-$130
Available dates: 1992-1996

LARGE ELEPHANT

This large model is decorated in the well-known Old Imari design with other decoration on the head and legs being interpretations of traditional Indian ornaments and includes a richly decorated Howdah. It was introduced with a complementary small elephant in 1990 and both are still available.

Launch Price: £295
Current Price: £460/$RRP
Available dates: 1990-Cur

LARGE ELEPHANT (GUMPS)

This version of the large Elephant had solid gold banding between the panels rather than the twin bands with white centre of the original and was only sold through Gumps of San Francisco in 1990. Very few, if any, have arrived back in the United Kingdom.

Launch Price: £325
Secondary Value: £600-£1000/$960-$1600
Available dates: 1992

LARGE ELEPHANT (HARRODS)

This version of the large Elephant incorporated the Harrods green and the Harrods logo and was sold in a limited edition of 150 in 1999 to celebrate the store's 150th anniversary.

Launch Price: £495
Secondary Value: £700-£800/$1120-$1280
Available dates: 1999

LARGE INDIAN ELEPHANT (MULBERRY)

At last an Elephant with grey skin! Commissioned by Mulberry Hall of York in 1997, this version of the paperweight had a limited edition of 500. Richly caparisoned in robes of blues, greens, turquoise and gold using patterns inspired by miniature paintings and early textiles of the Indian sub-continent to symbolise British India at its Peak. This representation is much more the working cousin to the Imari decorated versions.

Launch Price: £595
Secondary Value: £600-£800/$960-$1280
Available dates: 1997

LEICESTER FOX

Commissioned by Wheelers of Loughborough in 1999 in a limited edition of 1500, this is another variation on the fox model. It is most attractive, decorated in a more natural brownish orange seated on lilies in the field.

Launch Price: £80
Secondary Value: £100-£150/$160-$240
Available dates: 1999

LION

The seated male lion is decorated in gold and red fur on a white background and is depicted on a base representing the grasses of the plains where the animals dwell. A small grey mouse is shown between the fore and hind legs in recognition of the Aesop fable. The 1996 pre-launch Harrods version has the company logo on the fore leg near the mouse and has a premium of 10% to 20%. It was finally withdrawn in 2000.

Launch Price: £199
Secondary Value:
£250-£310/$400-$495
Available dates: 1996-2000

LITTLE OWL

A small paperweight representing the standing owl. This model is quite endearing for its realistic and lavish decoration in blue, red and gold feathers highlighted by the strong use of gold lining to form the outlines of the wings and eyes. Introduced in as a signature edition of 1000 by John Sinclair in 1998 it joined the main range and is still available.

Launch Price: £59.95
Current Price: £67/$RRP
Available dates: 1998-Cur

LLAMA

The Collectors Guild exclusive for 2001, the Llama was modelled and designed by John Ablitt. The inspiration for the decoration comes from the South American Indian weavings and features the earthy colours and geometric patterns of their style. A pre-Columbian gold pendant adorns the Llama's neck. It was only available in 2001.

Launch Price: £95
Current Price: £95/$RRP
Available dates: 2001

MADAGASCAR TORTOISE

The third in the second series of John Sinclair's special editions called "Endangered Species", this paperweight is a new colourway on the turtle. It may easily told apart from the imari decorated original as this model comes with a certificate and has bright red, yellow and gold sunbursts decorated onto its shell. It was produced in a limited edition of 1000 in the year 2000.

Launch Price: £89
Secondary Value: £120-£150/$190-$240
Available dates: 2000

MAJESTIC CAT

An event version of the Cat decorated with pale blue and gold swirls to represent the fur, developed by Carmen Roome for RCD roadshow events in 1997. A limited edition of 3500, it is quite an appealing colourway for this model.

Launch Price: £89.95
Secondary Value: £140-£180/$225-$290
Available dates: 1997

MALLARD

A relatively large paperweight this somewhat awkward representation of the mallard drake doesn't quite match the proportions of the real thing. It has the characteristic green head, yellow beak and blue flashes on the wings with the remainder being decorated in browns and gold. Introduced in 1997 it is still available.

Launch Price: £69.95
Current Price: £86/$RRP
Available dates: 1997-Cur

MANDARIN DUCK

Introduced in 1997 with the mallard, this is a much more successful representation. Decorated in glorious Technicolor with oranges, reds, blues, greens and gold, this duck by John Ablitt is most desirable. Introduced in 1997, it is still available.

Launch Price: £69.95
Current Price: £86/$RRP
Available dates: 1997-Cur

MEADOW RABBIT

A delightful reworking of the rabbit by Tien Manh Dinh to mark the Chinese year of the Rabbit. This paperweight has a fresh appeal with a decoration of wild flowers and grasses in reds, greens and gold. It was the complimentary gift for Guild members in 1999. It should not be confused with the Rowsley Rabbit.

Launch Price: £27.50
Secondary Value: £40-£60/$65-$95
Available dates: 1999

MILLENNIUM BUG

A bright blue representation of the scarab beetle with broad bands of gold highlighting, this paperweight is named after the computer scare which was related to the change of date at the end of the twentieth century. It was introduced in 1999 and was time limited until the end of 2000.

Launch Price: £45
Secondary Value: £50-£70/$80-$110
Available dates: 1999-2000

MILLENNIUM DOVE

Produced in 2000 ahead of the standard model for Goviers, thereby setting an unusual precedent. This paperweight is a new colourway on the Turtle Dove which has predominantly blue feathers on a white body with gold detailing, red and orange tail feathers. It was issued as a signature edition with a special backstamp limited to 1500 pieces.

Launch Price: £95
Secondary Value:
£90-£120/$145-$190
Available dates: 2000

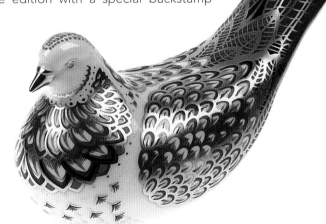

MOLE

The front half of the mole, in cobalt blue and gold emerges from a white mound decorated with red flowers, green leaves and golden grass of the English meadow. This model was the 1995 paperweight exclusive to members of the Collectors club.

Launch Price: £45
Secondary Value: £150-£200/$240-$320
Available dates: 1995

MONKEY AND BABY

Launched for the year of the monkey in 1992 and withdrawn in 1994 this model represents a seated monkey holding its baby. It is richly decorated in red and gold with touches of cobalt blue and is one of the more universally appealing models.

Launch Price: £89.95
Secondary Value: £150-£180/$240-$290
Available dates: 1992-1994

MULBERRY HALL FROG

One of the more successful private commissions done for Mulberry Hall in York, this paperweight is smaller than the standard frog and is brilliantly decorated in greens, blues and gold. Produced in a limited edition of 500 in 1996, it sold slowly to start with but is now highly sought after.

Launch Price: £89.95
Secondary Value: £490-£560/$785-$895
Available dates: 1996

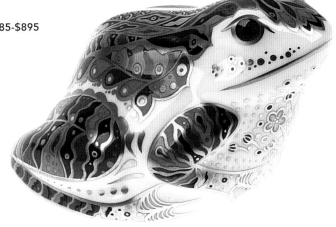

NANNY GOAT

Introduced in 2000 as the Royal Crown Derby Visitor Centre exclusive, the Nanny Goat is a small paperweight with a rich red and gold fleece standing in a field of grass. It comes with a certificate.

Launch Price: £85
Current Price: £85/$RRP
Available dates: 2000-Cur

NESTING BULLFINCH

Pre-launched by Bennets of Derby with a gold backstamp in 1996, the Nesting Bullfinch joined the main range in 1997 and was withdrawn two years later. This was the first of a surfeit of nesting birds, each of which sits on a "nest" and is decorated in the style of the standard bird in the range.

Launch Price: £51.95
Secondary Value: £50-£70/$80-$110
Available dates: 1997-1999

NESTING CHAFFINCH

Issued only in 1997 as the Guild exclusive piece for the year, it echoes the colours of the standard Chaffinch. It has a backstamp noting its exclusivity.

Launch Price: £52.95
Secondary Value: £50-£70/$80-$110
Available dates: 1997

NESTING GOLDFINCH

First issued in 1997 and withdrawn in 1999, this goldfinch is decorated in the same manner as the standard model but is draped over a "nest" of oak branches.

Launch Price: £52.95
Secondary Value: £50-£70/$80-$110
Available dates: 1997-1999

NESTING ROBIN

This fourth nesting bird was introduced in 1997 and was withdrawn last in 2000. Decorated in the same manner as the standard Robin manner, it is perched on a festive "nest" which resembles the Holly and the Ivy.

Launch Price: £52.95
Secondary Value: £60-£80/$95-$130
Available dates: 1999-2000

NUTHATCH

An interesting and popular representation of this pretty garden bird, the Nuthatch is decorated with thick gold bands blue back feathers and a pink breast overlaid with brown and gold feathers. First issued in 1999, it is still available.

Launch Price: £56
Current Price: £68/$RRP
Available dates: 1999-Cur

OLD IMARI FROG

This reworking of the original frog paperweight in lavish Old Imari patterns was only available at Royal Crown Derby events in 1998. Produced in a limited number of 4500 each one is individually numbered and many will also carry a signature from the event.

Launch Price: £80
Secondary Value: £90-£110/$145-$175
Available dates: 1998

OLD IMARI HONEY BEAR

Pre-launched in an issue of 250 in 1997 by Goviers with a special backstamp this is a reworking of the Honey Bear. A lavish paperweight it is decorated in the Old Imari 1128 pattern and is an improvement on the original decoration. It joined the main range and is still in production.

Launch Price: £89.95
Current Price: £108/$RRP
Available dates: 1997-Cur

OLD IMARI POLAR BEAR

Pre-launched in an issue of 500 in 1998 by Goviers with Sue Rowes signature and a certificate. This was the first appearance of the Polar Bear model in the main range which had been first seen as a Posie paperweight. A very attractive paperweight, it joined the main range and was then withdrawn after a short run in 2000.

Launch Price: £89.95
Secondary Value: £100-£200/$160-$320
Available dates: 1998-2000

OLD IMARI SNAKE

This model is a reissue of the Snake paperweight modelled by Robert Jefferson, re-designed by Sue Rowe to make use of the rich traditional Old Imari design in order to celebrate the Chinese year of the snake in 2001. To my mind this is how the snake should have been decorated in the first place, a wonderful piece.

Launch Price: £105
Current Price: £108/$RRP
Available dates: 2001-Cur

ORCHARD HEDGEHOG

Issued as the Collectors Guild exclusive in 2000, the Orchard Hedgehog is a new model for the animal. It is charmingly decorated in a leafy design of reds, blues and gold with apples superimposed to reflect the country lore that the animal takes home fruit on its spines.

Launch Price: £64
Secondary Value: £80-£100/$130-$160
Available dates: 2000

OTTER

Launched as a pre-release by the Guild of China and Glass in 2001 as a gold backstamp issue, modelled by Mark Delf and decorated by Sue Rowe closely follows the wild animal posing on the edge of the water in the weeds. Though heavily guilded, its pelt is coloured in the softer reds of the Deer but speckled with blue red and yellow to represent the drops of water.

Launch Price: £115
Current Price: £115/$RRP
Available dates: 2001-Cur

OWL

The least natural of all the paperweights this model is loosely based on a terracotta version from Corinth of about 7th century BC symbol of Athene, Goddess of Wisdom. The owl was first issued in 1981 and was withdrawn in 1992.

Launch Price: £45
Secondary Value: £250-£300/$400-$480
Available dates: 1981-1992

PANDA

A seated representation of the World Wildlife emblem, this model is decorated in blue, black and gold fur with gold and red bamboo on its back and tummy. Introduced in 1994 it is still available.

Launch Price: £69.95
Current Price: £84/$RRP
Available dates: 1994-Cur

PARTRIDGE

Available as the Royal Crown Derby Event piece in 1999 only, the Partridge is decorated in the same manner as the pheasant in rich blues and reds enhanced by gold. Designed and modelled by John Ablitt, the intention was to limit the production to 4500.

Launch Price: £70
Secondary Value:
£60-£80/$95-$130
Available dates: 1999

PENGUIN

Produced between 1981 and 1992 this Japan version of the "Emperor" penguin has a mazarine blue robe gilded with feathers and its white breast displays an heraldic ermine device.

Launch Price: £45
Secondary Value: £200-£225/$320-$360
Available dates: 1981-1992

PENGUIN & CHICK

An emotive model of the penguin in a pose ready to feed its chick, which is shown painted huddling between its feet for warmth. With a black head which shades to blue down the back, it is decorated with snowflakes and a flash of yellow, it is quite desirable.

Launch Price: £66
Current Price: £75/$120
Available dates: 1998

PHEASANT

Introduced in 1983 this lavish representation of the exotic pheasant is richly coloured in reds, blues and gold. A popular model, it is still available today.

Launch Price: £49
Secondary Value: £110-£130/$175-$210
Available dates: 1983-1998

PICKWORTH PIGLET

The fourth in a series exclusive to Sinclairs, the Pickworth Piglet is a revised colourway on the Sitting Piglet. Decorated with flowers the body colour is a distinctive pink.

Launch Price: £56
Current Price: £56/$RRP
Available dates: 2001-Cur

PIG

Mainly white with an Imari pattern this version of the Gloucester Old Spot breed of pig was available between 1985 and 1991. It was not an especially attractive model.

Launch Price: £45
Secondary Value: £180-£250/$290-$400
Available dates: 1985-1991

PIGLET

A much more successful interpretation of this animal than the earlier Pig, this piglet is portrayed seated on a disk, mainly white with rich Imari decoration. Introduced in 1996 it was withdrawn in 1999.

Launch Price: £39.95
Secondary Value: £50-£70/$80-$110
Available dates: 1996-1999

PLATYPUS

Also introduced for the Australian Bicentenary, this peculiar creature is shown standing on its rear feet and is decorated in a rich blue with a golden wattle, red and blue water lilies representing its life on land and in water.

Launch Price: £53
Secondary Value: £150-£250/$240-$400
Available dates: 1988-1992

PLAYFUL KITTEN

Another member of the cat clan, this kitten is portrayed on its back and is decorated in cobalt blue, gold and red to match the rest of the family.

Launch Price: £49.95
Secondary Value: £40-£60/$65-$95
Available dates: 1993-1996

POPPY MOUSE

An exclusive gift to those who join the Collectors Club in 1996 the Poppy Mouse is a different colourway on the Harvest Mouse model. The upper body shows the mouse's fur in pale blue and gold on white coming from a base of red poppies and cobalt blue ears of corn.

Launch Price: £25
Secondary Value: £100-£150/$160-$240
Available dates: 1996-1996

PUFFIN

This colourful and peculiar sea bird was introduced in 1996.

Launch Price: £59.95
Current Price: £80/$RRP
Available dates: 1996-Cur

PUPPY

Available as the complimentary gift for joining the Collectors Guild in 2001, the Puppy is an original, individual and most desirable paperweight modelled by Mark Delf and designed by Louise Adams. Richly decorated in traditional Derby reds and 22 carat gold, it features a beautifully crafted and most natural sleeping spaniel puppy.

Launch Price: £36
Secondary Value: £40-£60/$65-$95
Available dates: 2001

QUAIL

One of the original designs issued in 1981 the Quail was withdrawn in 1991. Produced in traditional Imari colours with an overall reddish hue it complements the pheasant well.

Launch Price: £41
Secondary Value: £70-£110/$110-$175
Available dates: 1981-1991

QUEENSLAND KOALA

The fourth in Sinclair's Endangered Species, this paperweight is designed by Sue Rowe as a new colourway, on the original Koala modelled by Robert Jefferson. Decorated in black, red and light blue with eucalyptus leaves under his chin and limited to an edition of 1000, it is highly sought after but, I regret to say, is less effective than the original on which it is based.

Launch Price: £89
Current Price: £89/$RRP
Available dates: 2001-Cur

RABBIT

One of the original designs first produced in 1981 and still available today, the Rabbit has a white background covered with an heraldic style of decoration based on gold with blue tippets of ermine.

Launch Price: £35
Current Price: £52/$RRP
Available dates: 1981-Cur

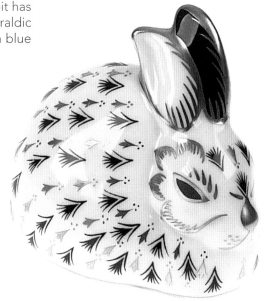

RAM

First introduced to Guild members in 1989 and launched worldwide in 1990, the ram was withdrawn in 1993. It was the first of a larger a more imposing model which was less likely to be used for the purpose of holding paper on a desk. Modeled as a Derby Ram, it is predominantly white with a cobalt blue face, fleece decorations in blue and gold and is shown standing in a field of red flowers.

Launch Price: £99
Secondary Value: £250-£350/$400-$560
Available dates: 1989-1993

RED BOW TIE TEDDY

Yet another variation on the Teddy Bear model. This was an exclusive to Goviers in a limited edition of 950 which bears "Goviers of Sidmouth Edition" on the base with the backstamp. This model has a red bow tie and a predominantly red Imari waistcoat with blue pads. It is very similar to the Regal Goldie Bear.

Launch Price: £59.95
Secondary Value: £120-£150/$190-$240
Available dates: 1997

RED FOX

A second colour way for the fox model this time in red and gold with green eyes, which had a short run between 1990 and 1993.

Launch Price: £33
Secondary Value: £450-£500/$720-$800
Available dates: 1990-1993

RED SQUIRREL

Yet another version of the squirrel which, despite its name has a pinkish, orange fur and has blue and turquoise leaf decoration rather than the deep russet brown of the natural animal. Nevertheless, it is an attractive paperweight which having been issued in 1998 is still available.

Launch Price: £60
Current Price: £67/$RRP
Available dates: 1998-Cur

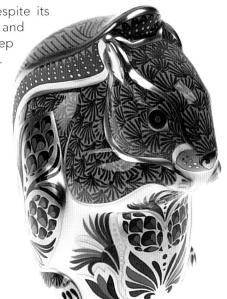

REGAL GOLDIE TEDDY BEAR

Yet another variation on the Teddy Bear model. This was an exclusive to three northern retailers in a limited edition of 1000 which bears its name on the base with the backstamp and come with a certificate. This model has a red bowtie and a predominantly blue Imari waistcoat with red pads. It is very similar to the Red Bow Tie Teddy.

Launch Price: £62.95
Secondary Value: £80-£120/$130-$190
Available dates: 1997

REINDEER

Modelled and designed by John Ablitt to complement the earlier Santa and Sleigh, which was left without motive power. Shown in a festive harness, baubles and colours predominantly of red blue and gold, it can easily be imagined that Rudolph himself posed for this piece.

Launch Price: £99
Current Price: £99/$RRP
Available dates: 2001-Cur

ROBIN

On the second of the garden birds, the traditional Imari colours are used to good effect. This model has a red feathery breast with blue and gold body. Introduced in 1989 it is still available today.

Launch Price: £35
Current Price: £50/$RRP
Available dates: 1989-Cur

ROCKY MOUNTAIN BEAR

Using the model of the Rocky Mountain Bear but decorating it in Imari pattern, this paperweight is better than the original and is still available today. It was pre-launched by Goviers in 1998 in a signature edition of 500 and then joined the main range in 1999.

Launch Price: £94
Current Price: £105/$RRP
Available dates: 1999-Cur

ROWSLEY RABBIT

The fifth of Sinclair's first series of specials, this new colourway for the rabbit paperweight is quite likeable with its red, yellow and gold small paisley fur sitting on meadow grasses and flowers. It can be confused with the Meadow Rabbit but has the words "An exclusive for John Sinclair" on the base.

Launch Price: £58.95
Secondary Value: £150-£180/$240-$290
Available dates: 1997

RUSSIAN BEAR

Though this bear was produced in 1991, it was only sold in Canada as it was felt there was no market for it in the UK. When secondary market pressure showed that there was, the factory decided that they would make it into a Guild Members piece in 1998. Showing a seated bear, it is a quite unattractive piece with trailing vines and flowers in red, blue and gold for decoration.

Launch Price: £85
Secondary Value: £70-£130/$110-$210
Available dates: 1991-1998

RUSSIAN WALRUS

Pre-released by Connaught House in 2001 in a limited edition of 1500 with a special backstamp and certificate, this is a new colourway on the original Walrus designed by Tien Manh Dinh. The dark striping of the back with coloured dots resemble the natural animal better than the original but it remains a slightly awkward model.

Launch Price: £115
Current Price: £115/$RRP
Available dates: 2001-Cur

SANTA AND SLEIGH

The second Christmas paperweight, this model depicts Santa tucked up tightly in a typical eastern European sleigh decorated with the presents that it is carrying. Issued in 1999 it is still available.

Launch Price: £90
Current Price: £95/$RRP
Available dates: 1999-Cur

SANTA CLAUS

Introduced in 1997 with a, John Ablitt, signature edition issued through Lawleys by Post in the same year, this paperweight is still available. It is produced in the form of the Russian doll and is a pleasant representation of that jovial yuletide fellow ready to perform his annual round of present giving.

Launch Price: £59.95
Current Price: £65/$RRP
Available dates: 1997-Cur

SAVANNAH LEOPARD

The second in John Sinclair's special edition called "Endangered Species", this paper-weight was modelled and designed by John Ablitt. Arguably one of the most evocative and powerful of all the paperweights, it is coloured in a sandy yellow with black and red spots crouching on a rock decorated with savannah plants and butterflies. It is a large model and was produced in a limited edition of 1000 in 1999 with a certificate.

Launch Price: £200
Secondary Value: £260-£300/$415-$480
Available dates: 1999

SCHOOLBOY TEDDY

Yet another variation on the Teddy Bear theme but smaller than the original bear. This time modelled and designed by John Ablitt, the bear is shown with schoolboy blazer and cap in blue with a red satchel on his back.

Launch Price: £60
Current Price: £60/$RRP
Available dates: 2001-Cur

SEAHORSE

Introduced in 1991 and withdrawn two years later this paperweight is a true representation of the animal. Standing on its tail, the white glaze is decorated with cobalt blue waves highlighted in gold and floating strands of seaweed in red.

Launch Price: £85
Secondary Value: £250-£350/$400-$560
Available dates: 1991-1994

SEAL

Introduced in 1983 and withdrawn in 1987 this is one of the least attractive of the paperweights. It represents the infant sea mammal but its normally pure white coat is enriched with a Japan interpretation of "flowers of peace".

Launch Price: £49
Secondary Value: £370-£400/$560-$640
Available dates: 1983-1987

SHEEP

Another attempt to celebrate the Chinese calendar saw the introduction of the sheep in 1991 and withdrawn in 1996. Once more the white glaze is decorated in a pale blue and gold fleece similar to the Ram and Lambs. However, in this case the curly fleece is covered in golden drops of early morning dew and the sheep does not have the cobalt blue face.

Launch Price: £69
Secondary Value: £120-£160/$190-$255
Available dates: 1991-1995

SIAMESE CAT

Another of the cat family, but more appealing than most, the enigmatic Siamese was introduced in 1996. It is decorated in an appropriate red, blue and gold paisley pattern on a predominantly white background which gives it that slightly Oriental flavour.

Launch Price: £55
Secondary Value: £60-£80/$95-$130
Available dates: 1996-2001

SIAMESE KITTEN

Introduced in 1996 to match the larger Siamese cat, it is still available today. It is depicted sitting, looking up with red, blue and gold paisley decoration on a predominantly white background.

Launch Price: £45
Secondary Value: £50-£70/$80-$110
Available dates: 1996-2001

SITTING DUCKLING

A small paperweight, this model has the duckling in a rather precarious pose. In nature it would represent that uneasy state of watchfulness prior to a dash for safety and consequently it appears somewhat unbalanced.

Launch Price: £48
Current Price: £54/$RRP
Available dates: 1998-Cur

SITTING PIGLET

This small and endearing paperweight is predominantly white with stylised decoration in blue and gold representing acorns, clover and truffles, the natural forage for the animal. It was introduced in 1999 and is still available.

Launch Price: £42
Current Price: £46/$RRP
Available dates: 1999-Cur

SLEEPING GINGER KITTEN

This revision of the colourway for the Sleeping Kitten produces another kitten to complement the Ginger Tom and Ginger Kitten with the same colourings. It is the second of a matching pair produced as a limited edition of 1500 for the Guild of Specialist China and Glass Retailers in 2000.

Launch Price: £56
Current Price: £56/$90
Available dates: 2001

SLEEPING KITTEN

Another kitten to fit in with the "family", this model is decorated in blue, red and gold Japan representations of the fur and markings. Introduced in 1991 it is still available today.

Launch Price: £49
Current Price: £62/$RRP
Available dates: 1991-Cur

SLEEPING PIGLET

This small and endearing paperweight is predominantly white with stylised decoration in red and gold representing acorns, clover and truffles, the natural forage for the animal. It was introduced in 1999 and is still available.

Launch Price: £42
Current Price: £46/$RRP
Available dates: 1999-Cur

SMALL ELEPHANT

The smaller elephant has more African style ears and a raised trunk but is richly gilded and decorated to match the larger one. Introduced in 1990 it is still available.

Launch Price: £109
Current Price: £155/$RRP
Available dates: 1990-Cur

SMALL ELEPHANT (GUMPS)

This small elephant has more gold than the standard model but is otherwise decorated in the same manner. They can most easily be distinguished from the standard by a thick gold line running down the back. Introduced in 1999, RCD stated that only 200 would be made available to UK collectors with remainder going to Gumps.

Launch Price: £199
Secondary Value:
£220-£260/$350-$415
Available dates: 1999

SMALL INDIAN ELEPHANT

This version of the small elephant is the colour compliment to the Mulberry Hall Indian elephant. Both are of a rose taupe hue and this one is richly caparisoned in robes predominantly of orange, red and gold in patterns reflecting the styles and customs of the Indian sub-Continent. It was produced in a limited edition of 950.

Launch Price: £245
Secondary Value:
£230-£260/$270-$415
Available dates: 1999

SNAIL

Available between 1985 and 1991 the classical spiral design of this model echoes the shell patterns of this garden mollusc and its food plants.

Launch Price: £45
Secondary Value: £100-£150/$160-$240
Available dates: 1985-1991

SNAKE

With the hooded head of the cobra, its looped body is decorated with diamond patterns in red, blue, jade green and gold. Introduced in 1989 it was withdrawn after a short run in 1992.

Launch Price: £62
Secondary Value: £130-£160/$210-$255
Available dates: 1989-1992

SPIRIT OF PEACE (DOVE)

Made to commemorate the anniversary of the end of the Second World War and fifty years of peace. This paperweight was commissioned by Wheelers, the first fifty have a double backstamp and are known as the "gold edition". It is a dove descending on a globe being consumed by flames with an inscription around it.

Launch Price: £430
Secondary Value: £2000-£5000/$3200-$8000
Available dates: 1995

SQUIRREL

Predominantly white, the squirrel is shown on its hindquarters nibbling at a nut. It is decorated with items that represent its natural habitat, hazelnuts, oak leaves, acorns and elderberries. Introduced in 1991 it is still available.

Launch Price: £49
Secondary Value: £50-£80/$80-$130
Available dates: 1991-1996

STONEY MIDDLETON SQUIRREL

The last of the six John Sinclair Derbyshire series, it was issued in 1997 and is another version of the squirrel. In this particularly striking colourway, the fur is pre-dominantly red and gold on a white body with mushrooms and acorns for added interest.

Launch Price: £59.95
Secondary Value:
£100-£130/$160-$210
Available dates: 1997

STRIPED DOLPHIN

This version of the Dolphin was introduced in 1999 by Connaught and is distinguished from the original by its pale blue, gold and white stripes. The base is decorated with other fish and symbolic waves making the whole less rich but more pleasing than the original. It is still available today.

Launch Price: £90
Current Price: £95/$RRP
Available dates: 2000-Cur

SWAN

Depicted sitting as though nesting, the base is decorated with water lilies, dragonflies and reeds of the typical waterside habitat of the Swan. The bird itself is predominantly white with golden and faint blue feathers. Issued in 1996 it was withdrawn in 1999.

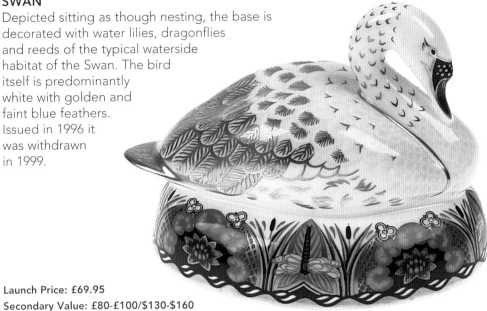

Launch Price: £69.95
Secondary Value: £80-£100/$130-$160
Available dates: 1996-1999

SWIMMING DUCKLING

An accurate representation of the bundles of fluff that can be seen in spring following their mothers along the river. It has brown feathers painted over the white body with a dark brown beak and blue top wing feathers. Issued in 1998 it is still available.

Launch Price: £48
Current Price: £54/$RRP
Available dates: 1998-Cur

TEDDY BEAR

This traditional representation of every child's teddy is portrayed seated. It is decorated with gold and blue curls of fur with a blue bowtie and the Imari pattern on the waistcoat and patches on the footpads. Introduced in 1997, it was the first of a rash of teddy bears.

Launch Price: £59.95
Current Price: £72/$RRP
Available dates: 1997-Cur

TEDDY BEAR (HARRODS)

Yet another variation on the Teddy Bear theme but this time exclusive to Harrods, in an edition of 1500. Once again modelled and designed by John Ablitt, the bear is shown in a dark green waistcoat and footpads with the Harrods logo on the left foot.

Launch Price: £60
Current Price: £60/$RRP
Available dates: 2001-Cur

TERRAPIN

Pre-launched with a special gold backstamp and signed certificate through the Guild of Specialist China and Glass Retailers in 2000, this is the first of a series of aquatic paperweights. It is an accurate representation of the animal with the shell decorated in two blues, red and black with gold detailing.

Launch Price: £75
Current Price: £75/$RRP
Available dates: 2000-Cur

TIGER CUB

One of the least appealing paperweights this model has the appearance of a bloated kitten rather than the svelte Tiger Cub. Introduced in 1993 and withdrawn in 1996, the stripes are in Imari red, blue and gold.

Launch Price: £63
Secondary Value: £60-£80/$95-$130
Available dates: 1993-1995

TURTLE

Introduced in 1983 and a long established favourite, the turtle is decorated with a variation of 1128 Old Imari on a white background.

Launch Price: £49
Secondary Value: £130-£150/$210-$240
Available dates: 1983-1998

TURTLE DOVE

Introduced in 2000 and still available, this fairly large and naturalistic representation of a sitting dove has heavily gilded feathers predominantly of red and green and can easily be confused with the rarer Millennium Dove issued by Goviers.

Launch Price: £99
Current Price: £105/$RRP
Available dates: 2000-Cur

TWIN LAMBS

This model has two lambs juxtaposed against each other. They are decorated in identical blues and gold to the single lamb. Introduced in 1993 they are still available.

Launch Price: £49.95
Secondary Value: £170-£210/$270-$335
Available dates: 1993-1997

UNICORN

The brainchild of Alan Morgenroth of Govier's of Sidmouth, this large paperweight was specially commissioned to celebrate the start of the third millennium. Limited to 500 copies, designed by Louise Adams and modelled by Mark Delf it is the first paperweight to incorporate metal. The horn is cast in a bronze alloy before being gilded. The seated mythological beast is predominantly white on a blue base, with golden mane and tail, wearing a splendid jewelled collar around its neck.

Launch Price: £180
Secondary Value: £210-£230/$225-$370
Available dates: 1999

WALRUS

Available between 1987 and 1991 this sea creature is decorated in a kaleidoscopic patchwork of Japan style decorations. Each tiny panel represents some aspect of the environment of this great sea creature, the Pole Star, sea anemones, calm and rough seas, and limpets which it may have prised from the rocks with the its tusks.

Launch Price: £57
Secondary Value: £150-£250/$240-$400
Available dates: 1987-1991

WAXWING

Another of the birds, this model is highly decorated in cobalt blue, pale blue and red in Imari style. Introduced in 1995 it is still available.

Launch Price: £45
Secondary Value: £60-£80/$95-$130
Available dates: 1995-Cur

WOODLAND PHEASANT

The Collectors Guild piece for 1999, the Woodland Pheasant is a pleasant re-visitation of the original design with the colours changed to add the excitement. It can be distinguished from the standard model by the colouring on its' back and head.

Launch Price: £78
Secondary Value:
£90-£110/$145-$175
Available dates: 1999

WREN

Another of the original designs produced in 1981 and still available today, the wren is a popular model. The plumage on the back of this tiny bird, which has a reputation for fearless courage, is designed in the style of ceremonial armour with gold on a blue ground. The remainder is in Imari and includes red.

Launch Price: £33
Secondary Value: £40-£60/$65-$95
Available dates: 1981-2001

ZEBRA

Introduced in 1995, this large paperweight departs from the normally associated colourways to dramatic effect. Showing the seated animal, complete with tick bird, its stripes are a combination of black and gold with a hint of red to the feathers of the bird. The base has a black, brown, red and gold Celtic design on a green background to suggest the open plains. There was a version issued with a Harrods backstamp which could be worth up to £750.

Launch Price: £150
Secondary Value:
£200-£250/$320-$400
Available dates: 1995-1998

Posies

This odd and somewhat esoteric issue of twelve paperweights, with the exception of the King Charles Spaniel, was issued mainly through the factory shop, at around £30, to capitalise on the success of the early paperweights. The main Posie range comprises objects for the Lady's dressing table in the country cottage style. The paperweights matched this

decoration but used the existing bodies of previously issued paperweights. There was one exception which has never been explained and that was the Polar Bear with had not previously been issued. It then had to wait until 1998 to join the main range as the Old Imari Polar Bear. The King Charles Spaniel was issued much later than the others rather as an afterthought. It was promoted as a special through Edwards of Derby as the last of the Posies in attempt to tie all the posies into the main range. However, this proved difficult as all the others were no longer available. The end result was that they created a rush in the secondary market and silly prices were being achieved for some very unattractive factory cast offs!

For those who wish to chase this offshoot I have listed the models that were issued in this fashion. Each may be recognised from the model in the main range issued as a white blank with the posie flower motif applied in random fashion all over. I have not ascribed a price to them as they are worth what you are prepared to pay. Most are not owned by collectors so they trade rarely and often at very silly prices. With the exception of the King Charles Spaniel which started at £32.95 the remainder originally sold for £25.00 each.

LIST OF MODELS

Posie Dragon; Posie Golden Carp; Posie Hamster; Posie King Charles Spaniel; Posie Owl; Posie Penguin; Posie Pig; Posie Platypus; Posie Polar Bear; Posie Quail; Posie Snail; Posie Snake.

Tropical Fish

Royal Crown Derby have always considered that this collection is separate to the paperweights which they so closely resemble. They are a series of six models, which were not terribly popular when they were in production. They are hollow, have a stopper and are each mounted on a pale blue seashell for a base but they were always sold as a separate collection in the catalogue. The price list shows paperweights with the definition "PAPBOX" prefix before a number whereas the Tropical Fish were designated "TROFIS". They are collectable in their own right but look distinctly out of place when put into a paperweight collection. All were available between 1990 and 1995 but sold slowly until they were withdrawn.

ANGEL FISH
Probably the prettiest of the series, the vertical bands of blue, green and gold scales with the white head perfectly set off this fish to best advantage.

Launch Price: £57
Secondary Value: £150-£200/
$220-$350
Available dates: 1990-1995

CHEVRONED BUTTERFLY
An odd looking, oval fish, it is decorated mainly in pale blue with golden scales overlaid and a dark blue band across the eyes.

Launch Price: £65
Secondary Value: £125-£145/$200-$230
Available dates: 1990-1995

GOURAMI

An oval-shaped fish but with a distinct tail and dorsal fin, the Gourami is decorated in red, grey and black with gold detailing.

Launch Price: £57
Secondary Value: £125-£145/$200-$230
Available dates: 1990-1995

GUPPY

Probably the least attractive of the series and one of the easiest to find. The Guppy is depicted rising out of the shell and has a somewhat bulbous appearance which is emphasised by a white horizontal band which curls round the gills. It has a triangular red and white striped dorsal fin and distinctive dark blue colouring which is highlighted with red and gold.

Launch Price: £57
Secondary Value: £70-£95/$110-$150
Available dates: 1990-1995

KORAN

The most difficult to find and a relatively attractive model. It has a distinct tail with the fins being painted in gold as part of the decoration. The white fish is the decorated with light and dark blue waves highlighted in gold with bands of golden scales.

Launch Price: £65
Secondary Value: £125-£145/$200-$225
Available dates: 1990-1995

SWEET LIPS

Another easy fish to find, in another somewhat awkward design. Decorated in red and gold horizontal stripes at the rear, it has an airship like appearance with a swept back dorsal fin and rounded tail. The head is decorated in red, blue and gold over the white with geometric patterns that combine to make the disconcerting whole.

Launch Price: £57
Secondary Value: £85-£130/$135-210
Available dates: 1990-1995

Crowns

CROWN
This Queens Crown was produced, and only available, in 1990 to celebrate the centenary of the granting, by Queen Victoria in 1890, of the Royal Warrant to the Crown Derby factory. It has blue velvet under the gold supports with a double band of white pearls leading to the orb at the top. Each one has a certificate and comes in a tall octagonal velvet box.

Launch Price: £90
Secondary Value: £600-£750/$960-$1200
Available dates: 1990

QUEEN MOTHER'S CROWN
This Kings Crown was issued as a limited edition of 1000, by Goviers, in 2000 to commemorate the 100th birthday of Her Majesty Queen Elizabeth the Queen Mother. Each crown is numbered and has a certificate. It has red velvet under the under the gold supports with a single band of white pearls leading to the boss at the top.

Launch Price: £195
Secondary Value: £400-£500/$640-$800
Available dates: 2000

Year Cyphers

This cypher is normally found under the glaze on the base of a paperweight to indicate the year in which it was manufactured. The fact that it is missing does not necessarily mean that anything is amiss, though there should be another form indicating the year of manufacture.

1981	XLIV
1982	XLV
1983	XLVI
1984	XLVII
1985	XLVIII
1986	XLIX
1987	L
1988	LI
1989	LII
1990	LIII
1991	LIV
1992	LV
1993	LVI
1994	LVII
1995	LVIII
1996	LIX
1997	LX
1998	LXI
1999	LXII
2000	MM
2001	MMI
2002	MMII
2003	MMIII
2004	MMIV
2005	MMV
2006	MMVI
2007	MMVII
2008	MMVIII
2009	MMIX
2010	MMX

ALPHABETICAL INDEX BY NAME

Letters in brackets indicate a Paperweight from a
particular retail outlet as follows:
(B) Bennets of Derby
(G) Goviers of Sidmouth
(H) Harrods of London
(MH) Mulberry Hall of York
(RD) Royal Doulton
(JS) John Sinclair of Bakewell and Sheffield

(PJ) Peter Jones of Derby
(W) Wheelers of Loughborough

CROWNS
Crown Derby
Queen Mother's (G)

GENERAL PAPERWEIGHTS
Armadillo
Ashbourne Hedgehog (JS)
Baby Rabbit
Baby Rowsley Rabbit (JS)
Badger
Bakewell Duck (JS)
Bakewell Duckling (JS)
Bald Eagle
Barn Owl
Beaver
Bengal Tiger
Bengal Tiger Cub
Bengal Tiger Cub (B)
Blue Jay
Blue Ladybird
Blue Tit
Bluebird
Brown Pelican
Brown Pelican (Hadleigh)
Bull
Bulldog

Buxton Badger (JS)
Camel
Camel (H)
Carolina Duck
Cat
Catnip Kitten (Guild)
Chaffinch
Cheshire Cat (JS)
Chicken
Chipmunk
Cockerel
Computer Mouse
Contented Cat
Contented Kitten
Coot
Country Mouse
Crab
Cromer Crab (RD)
Dappled Quail
Debonair Bear
Deer
Derby County Ram
Derby Ram
Derby Wren (Guild)
Derbyshire Duckling (JS)
Dolphin
Donkey
Donkey "Thistle" (G)
Dormouse
Dragon

Dragon of Good Fortune (PJ)
Dragon of Happiness (PJ)
Drummer Bear
Drummer Bear (G)
Duck
Duck Billed Platypus
Fawn
Firecrest (Guild)
Fox
Frog
Garden Snail
Ginger Kitten
Ginger Tom
Goldcrest
Golden Carp
Golden Pheasant
Grey Kitten (Guild)
Grey Squirrel (Debenhams)
Hamster
Harbour Seal
Harvest Mouse
Hedgehog
Heraldic Lion
Honey Bear
Horse
Humming Bird
Imari Dormouse
Imperial Panda (JS)
Kangaroo and Baby
King Charles Spaniel
Kingfisher
Kitten
Koala
Koala and baby
Lady Amhurst Pheasant
Ladybird - 2 Spot
Ladybird - 7 Spot
Lamb
Large Elephant
Large Elephant (Gumps)
Large Indian Elephant (MH)
Leicester Fox (W)
Lion
Lion (H)

Little Owl
Little Owl (JS)
Llama
Madagascar Tortoise (JS)
Majestic Cat
Mallard
Mandarin Duck
Meadow Rabbit
Millenium Bug
Millenium Dove (G)
Mole
Monkey and Baby
Mulberry Hall Frog (MH)
Nanny Goat
Nesting Bullfinch
Nesting Bullfinch (B)
Nesting Chaffinch
Nesting Goldfinch
Nesting Robin
Nuthatch
Old Imari Frog
Old Imari Honey Bear
Old Imari Honey Bear (G)
Old Imari Polar Bear
Old Imari Polar Bear (G)
Old Imari Snake
Orchard Hedgehog
Otter
Owl
Panda
Partridge
Penguin
Penguin & Chick
Pheasant
Pickworth Piglet (JS)
Pig
Piglet
Platypus
Playful Kitten
Poppy Mouse
Puffin
Puppy
Quail
Queensland Koala (JS)

Rabbit
Ram
Red Bow Tie Teddy (G)
Red Fox
Red Squirrel
Regal Goldie Teddy Bear (Hadley)
Reindeer
Robin
Rocky Mountain Bear
Rocky Mountain Bear (G)
Rowsley Rabbit (JS)
Russian Bear
Russian Walrus (Connaught)
Santa and Sleigh
Santa Claus
Santa Claus (Lawleys)
Savannah Leopard (JS)
Schoolboy Teddy
Seahorse
Seal
Sheep
Siamese Cat
Siamese Kitten
Sitting Duckling
Sitting Piglet
Sleeping Ginger Kitten
Sleeping Kitten
Sleeping Piglet
Small Elephant
Small Elephant (Gumps)
Small Indian Elephant (MH)
Snail
Snake
Spirit of Peace (Dove) (W)
Squirrel
Stoney Middleton Squirrel (JS)
Striped Dolphin
Striped Dolphin (Connaught)
Swan
Swimming Duckling
Teddy Bear
Teddy Bear (H)
Terrapin
Tiger Cub
Turtle

Turtle Dove
Twin Lambs
Unicorn (G)
Walrus
Waxwing
Woodland Pheasant
Wren
Zebra
Zebra (H)

POSIES
Posie Dragon
Posie Golden Carp
Posie Hamster
Posie King Charles Spaniel
Posie Owl
Posie Penguin
Posie Pig
Posie Platypus
Posie Polar Bear
Posie Quail
Posie Snail
Posie Snake

TROPICAL FISH
Angel Fish
Chevroned Butterfly
Gourami
Guppy
Koran
Sweet Lips

INDEX BY GROUPS

Imari Dormouse
Ladybird - 2 Spot
Ladybird - 7 Spot
Leicester Fox (W)
Meadow Rabbit
Mole
Orchard Hedgehog
Poppy Mouse
Rabbit
Red Fox
Red Squirrel
Rowsley Rabbit (JS)
Snail
Snake
Squirrel
Stoney Middleton Squirrel (JS)

CROWNS
Crown Derby
Queen Mother's (Goviers)

DOGS
Bulldog
King Charles Spaniel
Puppy

FARM ANIMALS
Bull
Chicken
Cockerel
Derby County Ram
Derby Ram
Donkey
Donkey "Thistle" (G)
Horse
Lamb
Nanny Goat
Pickworth Piglet (JS)
Pig
Piglet
Ram
Sheep
Sitting Piglet
Sleeping Piglet
Twin Lambs

HOUSEHOLD
Computer Mouse
Debonair Bear
Dragon
Dragon of Good Fortune (PJ)
Dragon of Happiness (PJ)
Drummer Bear
Drummer Bear (G)
Hamster
Herald Lion
Millenium Bug
Red Bow Tie Teddy (G)
Regal Goldie Teddy Bear
Santa and Sleigh
Santa Claus
Santa Claus (Lawleys)
Schoolboy Teddy
Spirit of Peace (Dove)
Teddy Bear
Teddy Bear (H)
Unicorn (G)

POSIES
Posie Dragon
Posie Golden Carp
Posie Hamster
Posie King Charles Spaniel
Posie Owl
Posie Penguin
Posie Pig
Posie Platypus
Posie Polar Bear
Posie Quail
Posie Snail
Posie Snake

SEASHORE
Crab
Cromer Crab (RD)
Dolphin
Harbour Seal
Penguin
Penguin & Chick
Russian Walrus (Connaught)
Seahorse

Seal
Striped Dolphin
Striped Dolphin (Connaught)
Walrus

TROPICAL FISH
Angel Fish
Chevroned Butterfly
Gourami
Guppy
Koran
Sweet Lips

WATERLIFE
Duck Billed Platypus
Frog
Golden Carp
Mulberry Hall Frog
Old Imari Frog
Otter
Platypus
Terrapin
Turtle

WILDLIFE
Armadillo
Beaver
Bengal Tiger
Bengal Tiger Cub
Bengal Tiger Cub (B)
Camel
Camel (H)
Honey Bear
Imperial Panda (JS)
Kangaroo and Baby
Koala
Koala and baby
Large Elephant
Large Elephant (Gumps)
Large Indian Elephant (M)
Lion
Llama
Monkey and Baby
Old Imari Honey Bear
Old Imari Honey Bear (G)

Old Imari Polar Bear
Old Imari Polar Bear (G)
Old Imari Snake
Panda
Queensland Koala (JS)
Reindeer
Rocky Mountain Bear
Rocky Mountain Bear (G)
Russian Bear
Savannah Leopard (JS)
Small Elephant
Small Elephant (Gumps)
Small Indian Elephant (M)
Tiger Cub
Zebra
Zebra (H)

STOP PRESS

The following paperweights were released just as we were going to press:

COTTAGE GARDEN CAT

Pre-released by Goviers as 'Clover', as a limited edition of 1500 with a special backstamp, this is another colourway on the Contented Cat. Delightfully done with cottage garden flowers and grasses round the base and coloured as a tabby, Sue Rowe has designed a pleasant addition to the ever expanding, cat range. This was accompanied by a Cottage Garden Kitten. **£78.00**

MOONLIGHT BADGER

A wonderful, new interpretation of the Badger, this time modelled and designed by John Ablitt. Shown as a foraging animal it wears 'the cloak of night' decorated by the leaves of the forest, the waxing and waning moon as well as the constellations of the Plough and Casiopia. **£95.00**

CRESTED TIT

The complimentary piece for the Members Guild in 2002, the Crested Tit is decorated with a certain amount of licence to ensure an attractive addition to the bird range. A rich blend of iron reds, blues and gold is used to highlight the back and wings, while the distinctive black crest and cheek markings are set off by the white base colour. **£27.50**

FRIESIAN COW

I suppose this domestic animal had to feature sooner or later as since time began the English potters have made china cows of one sort or another. Not to my personal taste, this large paperweight is threatened to become the first in a series. However, the paperweight is true to the animal and bears a white heart on the forehead as it is depicted seated on a field of buttercups, leaves, grass and seed pods. **£155.00**

RIVERBANK BEAVER

The Royal Crown Derby event piece for 2002, the Riverbank Beaver once again celebrates the national animal of Canada. Based on the original model by Robert Jefferson and designed by Sue Rowe, this new colourway is more colourful and attractive than its predecessor. Once more the maple leaf features heavily in the design in its autumnal colours while the pelt on the back is resplendent in blue with gold leaves. **£78.00**

BLACK SWAN(RD)

Only available through Royal Doulton outlets, in a limited and numbered edition of 2002, with 500 available to overseas markets, this model was heavily oversubscribed in the UK at issue. Produced to commemorate the Queen's Golden Jubilee, this is a resplendent new colourway on the original Swan, modelled by Mark Delf. The feathers are depicted in brown, beige and gold and around the base swim four signets to represent the Her Majesty's four children. **£125.00**

SCOTTISH TEDDY

This bear was available exclusively, with a gold backstamp, through Scottish retailers in

2002. General release with normal backstamps followed in 2003. It is similar in size to the schoolboy teddy and was modelled and designed by John Ablitt. Attired in Highland dress, the kilt is russet, there are Scottish thistles on its footpads with a red ribbon laid the top of its head and it was announced with the name 'Shona'.**£60.00**

PLUMSTEAD PIGLET(JS)
The fifth annual Sinclair paperweight, this is a new colourway on the Sleeping Piglet to compliment the Pickworth Piglet. Done in the same violent pink, the colour actually suits the model and comes quite close to the real thing. **£59.00**

COTTAGE GARDEN KITTEN(G)
Pre-released by Goviers as 'Lavender', as a limited edition of 1500 with a special backstamp, this is another colourway on the Sleeping Kitten. Delightfully done with cottage garden flowers and grasses round the base and coloured as a tabby, Sue Rowe has designed a pleasing addition to the ever expanding, cat range. This was accompanied by a Cottage Garden Cat. **£65.00**

IMARI RAM
The Visitor Centre exclusive piece for 2002, the Imari Ram is another representation of the Derby county mascot with a golden backstamp for the Jubilee year. Designed by Sue Rowe, it draws heavily on heritage and the Sherwood Foresters regimental mascot for its shape and colouring. **RRP NOT KNOWN**

COAL TIT
Modelled and designed by John Ablitt, the Coal Tit was launched in 2002. True to this common bird's distinctive markings it has a dark head and pale underbelly. Complemented by striking red, blue and gold wings and tail, flashed with white this is one of the better small bird paperweights. **£54.00**

ROCK HOPPER PENGUIN
This paperweight is one of six produced to commemorate the 21st Anniversary of the start of the paperweight range. **£75.00**

RED LEGGED PARTRIDGE
This paperweight is one of six produced to commemorate the 21st Anniversary of the start of the paperweight range. **£80.00**

SNOWY RABBIT
This paperweight is one of six produced to commemorate the 21st Anniversary of the start of the paperweight range. **£54.00**

LINNET
This paperweight is one of six produced to commemorate the 21st Anniversary of the start of the paperweight range. **£62.00**

TAWNY OWL
This paperweight is one of six produced to commemorate the 21st Anniversary of the start of the paperweight range. **£80.00**

TEAL
This paperweight is one of six produced to commemorate the 21st Anniversary of the start of the paperweight range. **£86.00**

JUBILEE CROWN(G)
The second of Goviers symbols of power and produced in the Golden Jubilee year in a limited edition of 950. A 'Queen's' crown, it has a bright scarlet inner to set off the gold and jewels of the crown itself. Originally most of these were sold to owners of the Queen Mothers Crown, so try to get the pair. **£195.00**

RHINO (JS)
Designed and modelled by John Ablitt, this is another large paperweight. Made as the fifth of John Sinclairs "Endangered Species" in a limited edition of 1000 with a special backstamp and numbered certificate. Predominantly white and blue with gold horns and detailing, the Rhino is depicted standing with head lowered. **£245.00**

THE YORKSHIRE ROSE ELEPHANT(PJ)
Another variation on the small elephant theme, the Yorkshire Rose elephant is very richly decorated in gold with a distinctive red rose of York placed on a blue ground in the chequerboard of the back cloth. **£165**

PLAYFUL GINGER KITTEN
This revision of the colourway for the Playful Kitten produces another complement for the Ginger Tom in the same colourings. Issued in 2002, it is the third of a matching series produced as a limited edition of 1500 for the Guild of Specialist China and Glass Retailers. **£56.00**

APPLEBY MARE
Designed by Louise Adams and modelled by Mark Delf this paperweight celebrates the annual Romany horse fair at Appleby. Royal Crown Derby has always had an attraction for the Romany people, especially in the Old Imari pattern. The pony is depicted standing and is predominantly white with a gold mane and Imari saddle cloth. Made for Sinclairs in a limited edition of 1500, it is numbered and has a certificate.**RRP not known**

GRECIAN BULL
The first in a series of mythological creatures commissioned by Connaught House in Nottingham, the Grecian Bull is a new colourway on the original Bull model. Presented as the black bull sent by Poseidon to King Minos, it has a white face, yellow and red saddle cloth and thick gold detailing. More imposing than its predecessor, it was produced in a limited edition of 750. **£345.00**

Crowns

JUBILEE CROWN
This Queen's Crown was issued in a limited edition of 950, by Goviers, to commemorate the 50th Jubilee of the accession of Her Majesty Queen Elizabeth II. Each crown is numbered and has a certificate. It has red velvet under the gold supports with a single band of white pearls leading to the boss at the top. **£195.00**